RECOGNISING ACHIEVEMENT

G C S E
Mathematics

Graduated Assessment

Stages 5 & 6
Homework Book

Authors

Howard Baxter

Mike Handbury

John Jeskins

Jean Matthews

Series editor *Brian Seager*

Hodder & Stoughton

A MEMBER OF THE HODDER HEADLINE GROUP

Orders: please contact Bookpoint Ltd, 130 Milton Park, Abingdon, Oxon OX14 4SB.
Telephone: (44) 01235 827720. Fax: (44) 01235 400454. Lines are open from 9.00 – 6.00, Monday to Saturday,
with a 24-hour message answering service. You can order through our website at www.hodderheadline.co.uk

British Library Cataloguing in Publication Data
A catalogue record for this title is available from the British Library.

ISBN 0 340 84695X

First Published 2002
Impression number   10 9 8 7 6 5 4 3
Year   2008 2007 2006 2005 2004 2003

Cover illustration by Mike Stones

Typeset by Macmillan India

Printed in Great Britain for Hodder & Stoughton Educational, a division of Hodder Headline,
338 Euston Road, London NW1 3BH by J. W. Arrowsmith Ltd., Bristol

Stage 5

The exercises in this book are designed to cover the last part of the specification for the Foundation tier of GCSE Mathematics and also the first part of the Intermediate tier. They should be used with the Graduated Assessment GCSE Mathematics course, stages M5 and M6.

Each exercise here matches the exercises in the Graduated Assessment Stages 5&6 Text Book. In the Text Book the exercises are usually in pairs, **A** and **B**. In this Homework Book they all have the letter **C**. Thus, for example, if you had been working on *Plans and elevations* in Stage 5 in class, the exercises would be 13.1A and 13.1B. The corresponding homework exercise is 13.1C.

You will find that these homework exercises are shorter than those in the Text Book but still cover the same mathematics. Some questions are intended to be completed without a calculator, just as in the Text Book. These are shown with a non-calculator icon in the same way. Doing these questions without a calculator is vital preparation for the first section of the GCSE paper.

The double exercises in the Text Book are there to give you extra practice. These homework exercises extend this idea. It is also a smaller book to carry home! If you have understood the topics, you should be able to tackle these exercises confidently as they are no harder than those you have done in class – in fact, in some cases the exercises here may be a little easier. See if you agree. More practice helps to reinforce the ideas you have learned and makes it easier to remember at a later stage.

If, however, you do forget, further help is at hand. As well as the Text Book and this Homework Book there is also a GCSE Mathematics for OCR Intermediate Revision Book and a GCSE Mathematics for OCR Foundation Revision Book. These are designed for use nearer to your GCSE exam to help you revise and explain the points you do not understand.

Other titles available:

GCSE Mathematics for OCR Foundation Revision Book   0340 85615 7
(for Foundation tier)

GCSE Mathematics for OCR Intermediate Revision Book   0340 85613 0
(for Intermediate tier)

Graduated Assessment Stages 5&6 Text Book   0340 84695 x

1 Cuboids

Isometric drawings

EXERCISE 1.1C

On triangular spotty paper make isometric drawings of these shapes.

1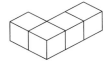

3

2

Volume of a cuboid

EXERCISE 1.2C

In this exercise, remember to give the units in your answers.

1 Calculate the volumes of these cuboids. All measurements are in metres.

a)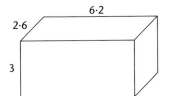

b)

Exercise 1.2C cont'd

2 A cuboid measures 12 cm by 5 cm by 4 cm.
Calculate its volume.

3 The base unit of a computer is a cuboid 18 cm wide, 40 cm long and 32 cm high.
Calculate its volume.

4 Find the height of a cuboid which is 15 cm long by 8 cm wide and has a
volume of 480 cm^3.

5 A concrete paving block is 10 cm wide, 20 cm long and 4 cm high.
How many of these blocks will fill a 1 metre cube?

Nets of cuboids

EXERCISE 1.3C

1 Draw a net for each of these cuboids on squared paper. All lengths are in
centimetres.

a)

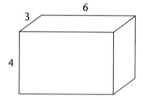

b)

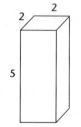

c)

Exercise 1.3C cont'd

2 Which of the nets below are for a cuboid? They are drawn accurately on squared paper.

a)

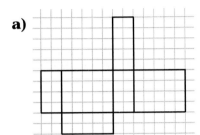

b)

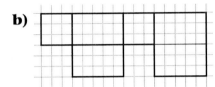

c)

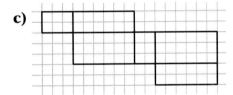

3 A packing case for a lawn mower is a cuboid measuring 80 cm by 60 cm by 40 cm. It has a top.
Draw a net of the packing case on squared paper. Use a scale of 1 cm to 20 cm.

4 A seed tray is 30 cm long, 20 cm wide and 5 cm high. It has no top. Draw a net for the tray on squared paper. Use a scale of 1 cm to 5 cm.

2 Rounding numbers and estimating

Approximating numbers

EXERCISE 2.1C

You can use a number line to help if you wish.

1 Write these numbers correct to the nearest whole number.

    a) 3·4   **b)** 5·9   **c)** 0·8   **d)** 23·8   **e)** 17·5   **f)** 17·49

    g) 514·2   **h)** 1469·7   **i)** 5638·07   **j)** 399·8

2 Round each of the following numbers:

    i)   to the nearest 10

    ii)   to the nearest 100

    iii)   to the nearest 1000.

    a) 1066   **b)** 23 629   **c)** 8912   **d)** 26 788   **e)** 46 950

3 Round each of the following numbers to the nearest million.

    a) 1 500 070   **b)** 5 020 469   **c)** 2 964 720   **d)** 4 199 689   **e)** 876 543

4 Write each of the following numbers:

    i)   correct to 1 decimal place

    ii)   correct to 2 decimal places.

    a) 80·9346   **b)** 5·1174   **c)** 4·39852   **d)** 0·03499   **e)** 649·0019

Exercise 2.1C cont'd

5 Use your calculator to work out each of the following to the stated accuracy.

a) $\dfrac{5}{6}$ (2 d.p.)   **b)** 5.5^2 (1 d.p.)   **c)** $\sqrt{24}$ (2 d.p.)

d) $\dfrac{64.3074}{2.91}$ (2 d.p.)   **e)** $\dfrac{15}{11}$ (1 d.p.)

EXERCISE 2.2C

1 Round each of the following to 1 significant figure.

a) 6·8   **b)** 7·32   **c)** 48·3   **d)** 0·63   **e)** 0·89   **f)** 4382

g) 587   **h)** 0·063   **i)** 0·0077   **j)** 0·000409   **k)** 99·83   **l)** 568 790

For the rest of the questions in this exercise show the approximation that you use to get the estimate.

2 Alan bought 22 cans of drink at 39p each. Estimate what he paid in total.

3 Tickets for firework display are £18·50 each. 4125 tickets are sold. Estimate the total value of the sales.

4 Estimate the answers to these calculations.

a) 6.32×7.12 **b)** $28.7 \div 6.3$ **c)** 48.3×32.1 **d)** $7896 \div 189$

e) 286×0.32 **f)** 18.9^2 **g)** $913 \div 196$ **h)** $4.7 \times 6.2 \times 9.8$

3 Metric and imperial units

Converting between metric units

EXERCISE 3.1C

Change the following.

1 **a)** 33 m to cm   **b)** 15 cm to mm

   c) 5·6 cm to mm   **d)** 5·62 m to cm

2 **a)** 2300 cm to m   **b)** 17 mm to cm

   c) 456 mm to cm   **d)** 580 cm to m

3 **a)** 6·3 kg to g   **b)** 5·2 tonnes
                                     to kg

   c) 83 g to mg   **d)** 3·2 litres
                                     to cm^3

4 **a)** 14 000 g to kg   **b)** 6400 ml
                                         to litres

   c) 8300 g to kg   **d)** 568 mg to kg

5 **a)** 7 m^2 to cm^2 **b)** 4·8 cm^2
                                               to mm^2

   c) 8·7 m^2 to cm^2 **d)** 0·4 cm^2
                                               to mm^2

6 **a)** 30 000 cm^2 **b)** 560 mm^2
           to m^2 to cm^2

   c) 8 500 cm^2 **d)** 586 000 mm^2
           to m^2 to cm^2

7

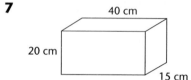

This empty fish-tank measures 40 cm
by 20 cm by 15 cm. Naeem uses a
2 litre jug to fill it.
How many jugfuls does he use?

Metric and imperial units

In all these questions use the approximate equivalents and give the answers to a sensible degree of accuracy.

1 The distance from Manchester to London is 200 miles. How far is this in km?

2 John put 42 litres of petrol in his car. How many gallons is this?

3 A car is 12 feet long. How far is this in metres?

4 A cow's average milk yield is 1·8 gallons per day. How many litres is this?

5 The length of a classroom is 6·5 metres. How many feet is this?

6 The Green family drinks 13 litres of milk per week. How many pints is this?

4 Solving equations

Two-step equations

EXERCISE 4.1C

Use flow charts to solve these equations.

1 $2x + 5 = 19$ **3** $3x + 5 = 11$ **5** $4x + 7 = 13$

2 $3x - 2 = 16$ **4** $5x - 2 = 6$ **6** $4x + 9 = 1$

EXERCISE 4.2C

Solve these equations.

1 $2x + 4 = 10$ **3** $3x + 4 = 10$ **5** $4x - 3 = 13$ **7** $2x - 6 = 3$

2 $2x - 7 = 11$ **4** $3x - 2 = 16$ **6** $4x + 2 = 14$ **8** $2x + 5 = 3$

EXERCISE 4.3C

Solve these equations.

1 $13 = 2x - 7$ **3** $17 = 5x - 13$ **5** $8 = 2x - 5$

2 $20 = 3x + 5$ **4** $25 = 7 + 6x$ **6** $1 = 3x + 7$

EXERCISE 4.4C

Solve these equations.

1 $8x - 9 = 15$ **3** $11 = 4x - 5$ **5** $6x + 5 = 65$ **7** $7x + 17 = 3$

2 $7 + 2x = 19$ **4** $6 = 2x + 8$ **6** $12 = 5x - 23$ **8** $12 = 4x + 3$

Powers, roots, multiples and factors

Powers and roots

EXERCISE 5.1C

1 Write down the square of each number.

   a) 4   **b)** 13   **c)** 34

2 Write down the square root of each number.

   a) 64   **b)** 225   **c)** 441

3 Write down the cube of each number.

   a) 1   **b)** 20   **c)** 11

4 Write down the cube root of each number.

   a) 64   **b)** 3375   **c)** 6^3

5 Work out these square roots.

   a) $\sqrt{529}$ **b)** $\sqrt{961}$ **c)** $\sqrt{1764}$

6 Work these out, giving your answers correct to two decimal places.

   a) $\sqrt{7}$ **b)** $\sqrt{67}$ **c)** $\sqrt{378}$

7 Work out these.

   a) 11^2 **b)** 14^2 **c)** 8^3 **d)** 100^2 **e)** $19^2 - 18^2$

Maps, bearings and scale drawings

Grid references

EXERCISE 6.1C

This is the sketch map of part of a town.

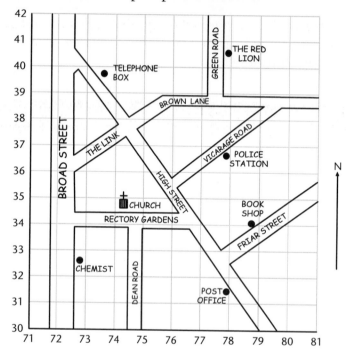

Answer these questions for the town.

1 Give the four-figure references for **a)** the post office **b)** the chemist **c)** The Red Lion.

Exercise 6.1C cont'd

2 a) Poppy walked from the telephone box to the post office down High Street. In what direction did she walk?

   b) What is the name of the second road on the left, which Poppy passed?

3 Which road runs east to west all the way along?

4 Graeme is at the chemist. He needs to go to the bookshop. Which route should he take?

5 Anne leaves the church and turns left. She then takes the first turn on the left, the second turn on the right and the first turn on the left. What road is she on?

Bearings

EXERCISE 6.2C

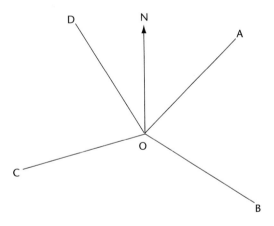

1 Measure the bearings of A, B, C and D from O.

2 I am walking due East. What bearing am I walking on?

3 A boat is sailing on a bearing of 75°. It turns 90° clockwise. What bearing is it now heading on?

Exercise 6.2C cont'd

4 The bearing of X from Y is 150°. Work out the bearing of Y from X.

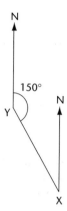

5 Town B is 10 km due South of town A.

Town C is 6 km from town A on a bearing of 105°.

a) Make a scale drawing of the three towns. Use a scale of 1 cm to 1 km.

b) Use your drawing to find

  i) the bearing of town B from town C

  ii) the distance of town B from town C.

Estimation

Estimating measurements

EXERCISE 7.1C

1 Estimate the length of this line.

_____

2 Estimate the size of this angle.

3 Estimate the mass of a house brick.

4 Estimate the amount of liquid in a mug of coffee.

5 Are the following statements reasonable?
If not, give something more sensible.

a) A doorway is 2 m high.

b) A car's petrol tank holds 30 ml of liquid.

c) Your school bag weighs 50 g.

d) My stride is 30 ft long.

e) It takes Beverley 10 minutes to walk 1 km to school.

Estimating area

Estimate the area of these shapes by counting squares.

1

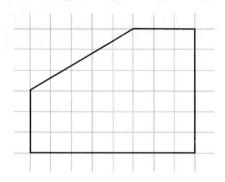

2

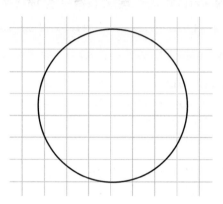

3

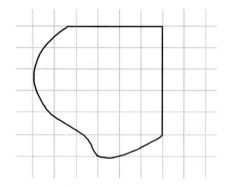

4

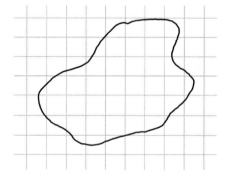

8 Pie charts

EXERCISE 8.1C

1 Draw a pie chart to show these costs for a holiday.

Travel: £100
Accommodation: £170
Food and drink: £110
Entertainment: £70

2 A class of students were asked what were their favourite colours. Here is what they said.

Orange 3   Green 4   Yellow 7
Red 9   Blue 5   Purple 2

Draw a pie chart to show this information.

3 This table shows how Javaid spends his day.

Draw a pie chart to show this information.

Activity	Hours
Sleeping	8
School	6
Travel	1
Playing & watching TV	6
Homework	2
Eating	1

4 Jane did a survey on how the students in her year came to school. These are her results.

Draw a pie chart to show this information.

Method of travel	Number of students
Walk	56
Bus	52
Cycle	38
Car	44
Train	10
Total	200

Information from pie charts

1 This pie chart shows what class 4A have for lunch.

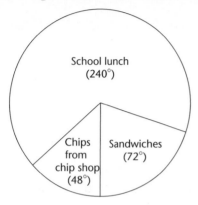

There are 30 students in the class. For each type of lunch, measure the angle and work out the number of students.

2 One day, the local library did a survey of the ages of the people using it. The pie chart shows the results. 275 people were surveyed. Measure the angles in the pie chart and calculate the number of people in each age group.

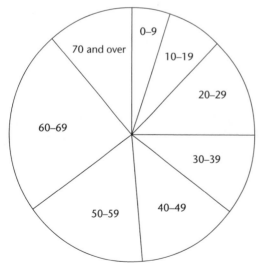

3 This pie chart shows how a charity spent its money in one year.

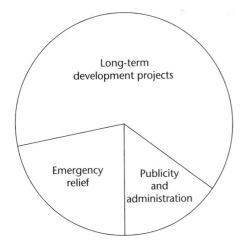

a) Measure the angle for publicity and administration and calculate the percentage spent on this.

b) The charity's total spending for the year was £3·5 million. How much was spent on emergency relief?

9 Fractions

Fractions

EXERCISE 9.1C

1 Fill in the blanks in these equivalent fractions.

$$\frac{3}{4} = \frac{}{8} = \frac{9}{} = \frac{30}{}$$

2 Write these fractions in their lowest terms.

a) $\frac{8}{10}$ **b)** $\frac{15}{18}$ **c)** $\frac{18}{24}$ **d)** $\frac{14}{28}$

3 Write these fractions in order, smallest first.

$$\frac{1}{2}, \quad \frac{3}{8}, \quad \frac{9}{16}, \quad \frac{3}{4}, \quad \frac{5}{16}$$

EXERCISE 9.2C

1 Fill in the blanks in these equivalent fractions.

$$\frac{4}{5} = \frac{}{10} = \frac{12}{} = \frac{36}{}$$

2 Write these fractions in their lowest terms.

a) $\frac{9}{15}$ **b)** $\frac{10}{30}$ **c)** $\frac{25}{40}$ **d)** $\frac{24}{32}$

For the rest of the questions, give all answers in their lowest terms.

3 Add these fractions.

a) $\frac{2}{7} + \frac{3}{7}$ **b)** $\frac{2}{5} + \frac{3}{10}$ **c)** $\frac{1}{4} + \frac{1}{5}$ **d)** $\frac{1}{3} + \frac{3}{10}$ **e)** $\frac{3}{8} + \frac{1}{6}$

Exercise 9.2C cont'd

4 Subtract these fractions.

a) $\frac{3}{8} - \frac{1}{8}$ **b)** $\frac{5}{8} - \frac{1}{4}$ **c)** $\frac{1}{3} - \frac{1}{8}$ **d)** $\frac{5}{6} - \frac{3}{8}$ **e)** $\frac{5}{8} - \frac{2}{5}$

5 Work these out.

a) $\frac{2}{5} + \frac{1}{4} - \frac{1}{2}$ **b)** $\frac{3}{8} + \frac{3}{4} - \frac{2}{3}$ **c)** $\frac{1}{3} + \frac{1}{4} + \frac{1}{5}$

6 Write these fractions in order, smallest first.

$\frac{3}{4}, \quad \frac{7}{12}, \quad \frac{19}{36}, \quad \frac{5}{6}, \quad \frac{4}{9}$

Mixed numbers

EXERCISE 9.3C

1 Change these top-heavy fractions to mixed numbers.

a) $\frac{10}{7}$ **b)** $\frac{12}{7}$ **c)** $\frac{11}{2}$ **d)** $\frac{13}{4}$ **e)** $\frac{11}{3}$

2 Change these mixed numbers to top-heavy fractions.

a) $1\frac{2}{7}$ **b)** $1\frac{5}{8}$ **c)** $7\frac{1}{2}$ **d)** $2\frac{3}{4}$ **e)** $3\frac{2}{5}$

3 Add, writing your answers as simply as possible.

a) $\frac{3}{4} + 1\frac{1}{2}$ **b)** $1\frac{1}{4} + \frac{3}{5}$ **c)** $2\frac{1}{5} + 1\frac{1}{3}$ **d)** $4\frac{1}{2} + 2\frac{3}{5}$ **e)** $1\frac{5}{6} + \frac{2}{5}$

4 Subtract, writing your answers as simply as possible.

a) $2\frac{7}{8} - \frac{3}{8}$ **b)** $3\frac{5}{6} - 1\frac{3}{8}$ **c)** $4\frac{1}{4} - 2\frac{1}{8}$ **d)** $3\frac{1}{2} - \frac{3}{5}$ **e)** $6\frac{1}{10} - 4\frac{2}{5}$

Listing events and probability

Covering all the possibilities

EXERCISE 10.1C

1 Gill and Chloe are discussing how to spend the evening. They want to read (R), watch TV (T) or go out (G). They can choose the same or different activities. Draw a table to show their possible choices.

2 In a game, two ordinary dice are thrown and the difference between the numbers on the dice is the score. Draw a grid with axes numbered 1 to 6 to show the possible outcomes. What is the probability that the score is 2?

3

Menu
First Course
Soup
Melon
Second Course
Spaghetti Bolognese
Lamb Biryani
Chicken & Mushroom Pie

John chooses a two course meal.
Draw a table to show all the possible choices.

Exercise 10.1C cont'd

4 Adam chooses a card from an ordinary
set of playing cards and notes its suit.
He replaces it and then chooses another.
The grid shows the possibilities.

♠	x	x	x	x
♦	x	x	x	x
♣	x	x	x	x
♥	x	x	x	x
	♥	♣	♦	♠

a) What is the probability that both of Adam's cards are clubs (§)?

b) Diamonds (♦) and hearts (') are red. What is the probability that both of
Adam's cards are red?

5

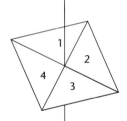 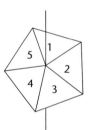

Habib spins these two fair spinners.

He adds together the two numbers they land on.

This sum is his score.

a) Draw a grid to show all the possible scores.

b) What is the probability that Habib's score is

   i) 9   **ii)** 6   **iii)** even?

11 Classifying quadrilaterals

Different quadrilaterals

EXERCISE 11.1C

1 Which quadrilateral has all angles equal to 90°, but not all sides the same?

2 Which quadrilateral has diagonals crossing at 90° and opposite angles equal?

3 Which quadrilateral has two pairs of sides equal that are not opposite?

4 Which quadrilateral has one pair of opposite sides parallel and the other pair equal?

5 Name the following shapes.

a)

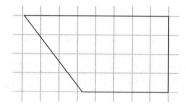

b)

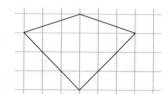

c)

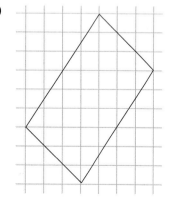

d)

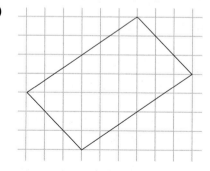

12 Simplifying algebra

Making it simple

Simplify these.

1 $p + p + p + r + r + r + r$

2 $x + x + y + x + y + x + y + y + x$

3 $2a + 3b + 5a - b$

4 $a \times a \times a \times b \times b$

5 $4x \times 3y$

6 $3a + 5b - 2a - 3b$

7 $5a^2 + 3a - 3a^2 + 6a$

8 $6p + 2q - 3 - 2p - 5q + 7$

Converting like terms and simplifying expressions

Simplify these where possible.

1 $7p + 3q - 2p - 2q$

2 $3x^2 - 2x + 4x^2 + 5x - 2x^2 - 7x$

3 $5x^3 - 3x^2 + 2x$

4 $3ab - 2ac - ab + 5ac$

5 $3x - 2y + 4z - 2x - 3y + 5z + 6x + 2y - 3z$

6 $3a^2 - 3ab - 2ab + 4b^2$

13 Plans and elevations

Plans and elevations

EXERCISE 13.1C

Sketch the plan and elevations of these solid shapes.

The arrows show the directions of the plan, P, front elevation, F, and side elevation, S, in each case.

1

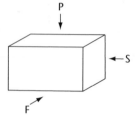

2

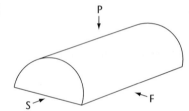

3

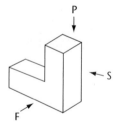

4

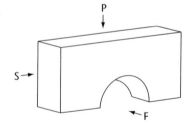

Draw accurately the full-size plan and elevations of this shape.
All dimensions are in centimetres.

5

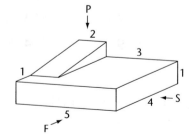

14 Interpreting statistical data and measures

Grouping data

EXERCISE 14.1C

1 The distribution of the weekly earnings of 30 children in their part-time jobs is shown in the table.

Draw a frequency diagram to show this information.

Pocket money (£x)	Number of children
$0 \leqslant x < 5$	5
$5 \leqslant x < 10$	10
$10 \leqslant x < 15$	8
$15 \leqslant x < 20$	6
$20 \leqslant x < 25$	1

2 Here are the lengths in millimetres of 30 tomato seedlings.

64	41	43	55	36	51	58	34	39	52
38	42	48	53	57	48	44	40	53	55
39	46	41	49	52	51	37	42	45	46

Use intervals 31–35, 36–40, and so on, to group these data in a frequency table. Then draw the frequency diagram.

3 Here are the prices of kettles in a catalogue.

£8·99	£11·90	£14·25	£11·99	£19·99	£19·75
£29·75	£39·50	£25·99	£27·95	£27·50	£29·50
£39·50	£48·50	£39·00	£49·50	£29·99	£39·50
£29·50	£29·50	£29·99	£33·50	£34·50	£34·50
£29·50	£29·50	£29·99	£34·50	£39·50	£44·00
£49·50	£39·50				

Use intervals of £5·01–10, £10·01–15·00, £15·01–20, and so on, to make a frequency table for these data. Then draw the frequency diagram.

Mean, median, mode and range of data

EXERCISE 14.2C

Look back at Exercise 14.1C and write down the modal class for each set of data.

EXERCISE 14.3C

1 For each of these sets of data, work out the mean, median and mode.
Give the mean to one decimal place.

a) 5 7 7 10 8 9 13 13 7   **b)** 11 13 25 15 16 13 18 15 11 17 11 15 11

c) 72 73 79 78 74 76 73 71

2 This frequency table gives the number of sweets in 20 bags of sherbert lemons.

Calculate the mean, median, mode and range for this data.

Number of sweets	Frequency
24	1
25	3
26	9
27	5
28	2

3 One measure of fitness is how far you can run in 12 minutes.
These are the distances, in metres, run by 15 members of a rugby team.

3125	2875	3254	2735	3489
2578	3536	3241	2876	3562
3456	2998	3147	3689	2521

Calculate the mean, median and range of these distances.

Comparing data

1 Greg and Pete are playing tennis. These are the statistics for the speed of first serves (in miles per hour) over a match.

	Greg	Pete
Mean	124·5	119·5
Median	123·1	121·2
Range	15·7	11·2

Compare the serving speeds of the two players.

2 The following marks were obtained by Alice and Bob in twelve spelling tests.

Alice: 6, 7, 9, 9, 10, 13, 18, 20, 21, 21, 22, 24

Bob: 3, 11, 12, 13, 14, 15, 16, 17, 17, 18, 21, 28

a) Find the median and the range of each set of marks.

b) Make two comparisons of the two sets of marks.

3 Hours of sunshine recorded at two seaside resorts are listed below.

Seashore: 8·6, 6·4, 12·3, 10·7, 9·5, 7·2, 8·8, 8·2

Cliff Top: 2·4, 0, 0, 5·6, 3·2, 9·8, 1·6, 0·4

a) Calculate the mean and the range of the two sets of data.

b) Compare the hours of sunshine at the two resorts.

15 Translations

Describing translations

EXERCISE 15.1C

Make a copy of this diagram and use it to answer Questions 1 to 4.

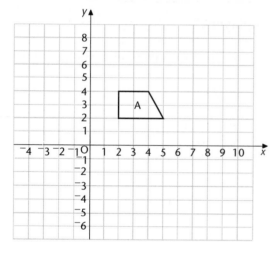

1 Translate shape A 6 squares down. Label it B.

2 Translate shape A 4 squares to the right and 3 squares up. Label it C.

3 Translate shape A 6 squares to the left and 4 squares up. Label it D.

4 Translate shape A 4 squares to the left and 7 squares down. Label it E.

Exercise 15.1C cont'd

Use this diagram for the next 4 questions.

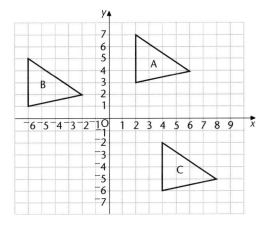

5 Describe the translation that maps triangle A onto triangle B.

6 Describe the translation that maps triangle A onto triangle C.

7 Describe the translation that maps triangle B onto triangle C.

8 Describe the translation that maps triangle C onto triangle B.

Fractions, decimals and percentages

Equivalence of fractions, decimals and percentages

EXERCISE 16.1C

1 Change the following fractions to decimals.

　　a) $\frac{7}{10}$ 　　**b)** $\frac{2}{5}$ 　　**c)** $\frac{11}{20}$

2 Change the decimals you found in Question 1 to percentages.

3 Change the following fractions to percentages.

　　a) $\frac{9}{10}$ 　　**b)** $\frac{17}{50}$ 　　**c)** $\frac{3}{25}$

4 Change the following percentages to decimals.

　　a) 28% 　**b)** 83% 　**c)** 4%

5 In a multiple choice test Aftab got $\frac{13}{20}$ of the questions right. Jamil got 63% of the questions right. Who got the most questions right?

Finding fractions and percentages

EXERCISE 16.2C

1 Work out $\frac{3}{8}$ of 672 m.

2 Work out 17% of £6300.

3 Work out $\frac{2}{11}$ of 3762 km.

4 Work out 27% of £12.

5 Ashley pays 6% of his wages into a pension fund.
How much does he pay in a month when he earns £1240?

17 Rotations

EXERCISE 17.1C

Draw the diagrams on squared paper.

1 Make two copies of this diagram and answer each part on a separate diagram.

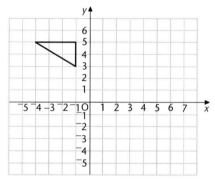

a) Rotate the triangle through 90° clockwise about the origin.

b) Rotate the triangle through 180° about the origin.

2 Make two copies of this diagram and answer each part on a separate diagram.

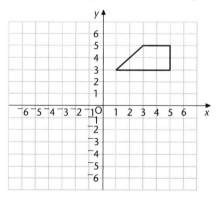

a) Rotate the quadrilateral through 90° clockwise about the origin.

b) Rotate the quadrilateral through 90° anticlockwise about the origin.

Exercise 17.1C cont'd

3 Make two copies of this diagram and answer each part on a separate diagram.

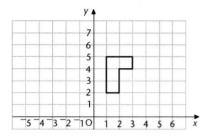

a) Rotate the shape through 180° about the point (3, 4).

b) Rotate the shape through 90° anticlockwise about the point (1, 2).

Drawing harder rotations

EXERCISE 17.2C

1

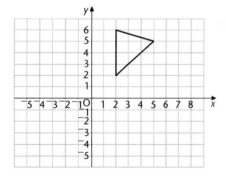

a) Rotate the triangle 90° anticlockwise about the point (5, 5). Label it A.

b) On the same grid, rotate the triangle 180° about the point (0, 3). Label it B.

Exercise 17.2C cont'd

2

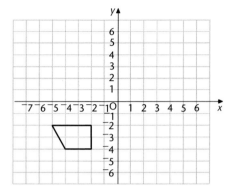

a) Rotate the shape 90° anticlockwise about the point (⁻5, ⁻2). Label it A.

b) On the same grid, rotate the shape 90° clockwise about the point (0, ⁻1). Label it B.

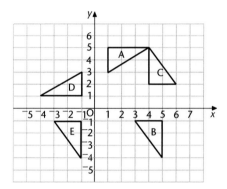

c) Describe fully the transformation that maps A onto B.

3 Describe fully the transformation that maps:

a) A onto B   **b)** A onto C

c) A onto D   **d)** D onto E

e) E onto B.

Expressing one quantity as a percentage of another

EXERCISE 18.1C

1 Find the following percentages.

    a) 28 as a percentage of 100

    b) 18 as a percentage of 150

    c) 6 m as a percentage of 75 m

    d) £3·80 as a percentage of £5

    e) £572 as a percentage of £880

2 Jenny gets a pay rise of £9. If she previously earned £150 per week, what percentage increase is this?

3 The audience in a cinema is 350. 139 of them are under eighteen.
What percentage is this?
Give your answer to the nearest whole number.

4 Lisa ordered a sofa which cost £450. She paid a deposit of £100.
What percentage deposit did she pay?

5 At a tennis club the membership consists of 85 women and 63 men.
What percentage are women?
Give your answer to the nearest whole number.

19 Sequences

For each sequence, find a rule and write down the next number.

1 5   9   13   17

2 22   17   12   7

3 10   100   1000   10 000

4 24   12   6   3

5 5   6   8   11

Write the first four terms of each of these sequences.

1 Start with 5 and add 4 each time.

2 Start with 1 and multiply by 10 each time.

3 Start with 12 and halve the number each time.

For the rest of the questions, the nth term is given.
Write the first four terms of each of these sequences.

4 $5n$

5 $4n - 2$

6 $3n + 100$

7 n^2

Stage 6

Contents

Stage 6

1 Using a calculator effectively

Calculators vary in how they do calculations

EXERCISE 1.1C

1 $15 \cdot 6 + 4 \times 3$

3 $127 \cdot 1 - 5 \cdot 6 \times 15 \cdot 1$

5 $16 \cdot 4 - 3 \cdot 7 \times 2 \cdot 1$

2 $18 - 2 \cdot 3 \times 5$

4 $7 \cdot 2 + 5 \cdot 1 \times 3 \cdot 4$

EXERCISE 1.2C

Give the answers exactly or to 3 significant figures.

1 $^{-}2 \cdot 7 + 3 \cdot 8 - 4 \cdot 9 + 2 \cdot 1$

3 $\dfrac{4 \cdot 6 - 3 \cdot 7}{9 - 7 \cdot 4}$

2 $(^{-}2 \cdot 1 \times 4 \cdot 2) + (2 \cdot 7 \times {}^{-}4 \cdot 6)$

4 $\dfrac{^{-}2 \cdot 7 \times 3 \cdot 9}{2 \cdot 6 + 3 \cdot 7}$

EXERCISE 1.3C

Work these out. Give the answers exactly or to 3 significant figures.

1 a) $3 \cdot 2^4$ **b)** $\sqrt[5]{984}$

2 $\sqrt{2^2 - 1 \cdot 8^2}$

3 $2 \cdot 3 \times 4 \cdot 7^2 - 4 \cdot 6 \div 2 \cdot 89$

4 $\dfrac{4 \cdot 67 \times 3 \cdot 91 - 4 \cdot 26}{6 \cdot 42 - 3 \cdot 97}$

EXERCISE 1.4C

Work these out.

1   3 m 14 cm + 5 m 27 cm + 2 m 89 cm + 3 m 14 cm

2   5 kg 500 g + 17 kg 314 g + 29 kg 863 g + 9 kg 744 g

3   4 min 15 sec + 9 min 12 sec + 8 min 54 sec + 16 min 23 sec

4   Find the mean of these 5 lengths.

   3 km 200 m, 3 km 190 m, 2 km 846 m, 2 km 641 m, 3 km 123 m.

Brackets and factors

Brackets

EXERCISE 2.1C

Expand these brackets.

1 $5(a + 2b)$ **3** $a(2a + b)$ **5** $^-3(2a - b)$

2 $3(x - 2y)$ **4** $2x(x - 3y)$

Factorising algebraic expressions

EXERCISE 2.2C

Factorise these expressions fully.

1 $2a + 6$ **3** $4bc - 2ac$ **5** $14abc - 21a^2b$

2 $3a^2 - 5ab$ **4** $5x^2 + 10xy$

3 Angles

Some basic angle facts

EXERCISE 3.1C

1 Two angles of a triangle are 40° and 75°. Work out the other angle.

2 Find the size of *a*, *b* and *c*.

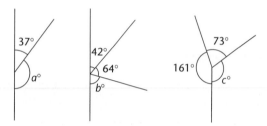

3 Find the size of *a*, *b* and *c*.

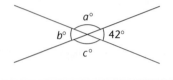

4 Copy and complete the table below.

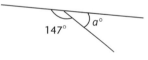

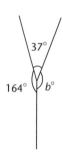

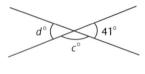

Angle	Size	Reason
a		Angles on a straight line add up to ....
b		Angles at a...
c		Angles ....
d		.... angles at a point are ....

5 Three angles of a quadrilateral are 147°, 23° and 101°.

Work out the size of the other angle.

Angles with parallel lines

1 Find the sizes of *a*, *b*, and *c*, giving your reasons.

2 Find the size of *d*, *e* and *f*.

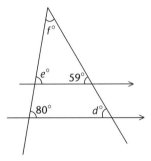

3 Draw a pair of parallel lines and a line crossing them.
Mark a pair of alternate angles.

4 Find the size of the lettered angles in this diagram.

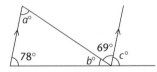

5 In a parallelogram ABCD, angle ABC is 49°. Sketch the parallelogram and clearly mark the size of each interior angle.

Exterior angle of a triangle

Work out the size of the angles marked with letters.

1 a)

b)

2 a)

b)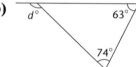

3 a)

b)

4 a)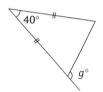

b)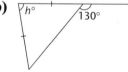

Angles in polygons

1 Three exterior angles of a quadrilateral are 125°, 68° and 95°.
Work out the size of the fourth exterior angle.

2 Four of the exterior angles of a pentagon are 62°, 55°, 68° and 105°.
Find the size of the other exterior angle.

3 Four of the exterior angles of a hexagon are 72°, 45°, 68° and 81°.
The other two exterior angles are equal. Find the size of each of them.

Exercise 3.4C cont'd

4 Work out the size of an interior angle of a regular octagon.
Show your working.

5 **a)** Work out the sum of the interior angles of a pentagon.

   b) Four of the interior angles of a pentagon are 140°, 120°, 100° and 60°.
   Work out the size of the other interior angle.

4 Probability

Probability of an outcome not happening

EXERCISE 4.1C

1 The probability that Eric will have meat for tea is 0·85.
What is the probability that he will not have meat for tea?

2 The probability that the traffic lights will be on red when I reach them is 0·45.
What is the probability that the lights will not be on red?

3 A fair die is thrown.

   a) What is the probability of getting a five or a six?

   b) What is the probability of not getting a five or a six?

4 A card is chosen at random from a pack of playing cards.

   a) What is the probability that it is a spade?

   b) What is the probability that it is not a spade?

5 The probability that David is absent from school is 0·05.
What is the probability that he is not absent?

Mutually exclusive outcomes

EXERCISE 4.2C

1 Nina, Christine and Jean are the only entrants for the maths prize. The
probability that Nina wins is 0·3, the probability that Christine wins is 0·45.
What is the probability that Jean wins?

Exercise 4.2C cont'd

2 At Millhouses Youth club, members can choose to play table tennis, badminton or not to play anything. The probability that Jake chooses table tennis is 0·65, the probability that he chooses badminton is 0·25. What is the probability that he chooses neither?

3 In a cricket match, the probability that Holbrook win is 0·23, the probability they lose is 0·47. What is the probability that they tie?

4 In an experiment, there are 4 mutually exclusive outcomes possible. These are A, B, C and D.
P(A) = 0·12
P(B) = 0·34
P(C) = 0·27

Find P(D).

5 Brian has a black, a green and a blue tie. He decides to wear a tie. The probability he selects the black tie is 0·28 and the probability he selects the green tie is 0·51. What is the probability that he selects the blue one?

5 Percentages

Fractions to decimals to percentages

EXERCISE 5.1C

1 Copy the following table and complete it.

Fraction	Decimal	Percentage
$\frac{3}{10}$		
$\frac{3}{5}$		
$\frac{7}{20}$		
$\frac{3}{8}$		
$\frac{5}{6}$		

2 Change these decimals to percentages.

a) 0·47   **b)** 0·82   **c)** 0·04   **d)** 0·425   **e)** 1·35

3 Change the following fractions to decimals.

a) $\frac{19}{100}$ **b)** $\frac{9}{50}$ **c)** $\frac{13}{20}$ **d)** $\frac{3}{100}$ **e)** $\frac{7}{4}$

4 Change the following fractions to percentages.

a) $\frac{7}{10}$ **b)** $\frac{3}{50}$ **c)** $\frac{7}{8}$ **d)** $\frac{6}{100}$ **e)** $\frac{9}{5}$

Expressing one quantity as a percentage of another

1 For each of the following, write the first quantity as a percentage of the second.

    a) 14 and 100   **b)** 6 and 50   **c)** 3 m and 5 m
    d) 27p and £1   **e)** £1·20 and £5

2 What percentage is 350 ml of 1 litre?

You can use a calculator in the next two questions if you wish.

3 For each of the following, write the first quantity as a percentage of the second. Give the answers to 1 decimal place.

    a) 14 and 84   **b)** 6 and 35   **c)** 2 m and 9 m
    d) 27p and 90p   **e)** £1·47 and £3·75

4 What percentage is 450 g of 3·5 kg?

Percentage increase and decrease

1 Joan's salary increased from £25 000 to £27 000.
What percentage increase is this?

2 Mitesh buys a bike for £350 and sells it for £300. What is his percentage loss?

3 Craig bought a printer marked at £56. VAT of 17·5% was added to this price. What was the price including VAT?

4 In a sale, everything was reduced by 35%. A coat was priced at £65 before the sale. What was the sale price of the coat?

5 In a savings account, 6% interest is added at the end of each year.
If £5000 is invested, what will the total be
a) at the end of one year   **b)** at the end of two years?

 Ratio

A reminder

EXERCISE 6.1C

Write these ratios in their simplest form.

1 3 : 9   **3** 18 : 24   **5** 10 minutes : 1 hour   **7** 60p : £5

2 4 : 6   **4** 54 : 24   **6** 50 cm : 2 m   **8** 450 ml : 1 litre

Using ratios

EXERCISE 6.2C

1 Share £4000 in the ratio 2 parts to 3 parts.

2 Share £2400 in the ratio 5 parts to 3 parts.

3 Tom and Niki share £4500 in the ratio 5 to 4. How much do they each get?

EXERCISE 6.3C

1 The ratio of A to B is 1 to 4.

 a) Find B if A is £300.   **b)** Find A if B is £800.

2 Concentrated orange and water are mixed in the ratio 1 to 5 to make squash.

 a) How much water should be mixed with 50 ml of concentrated orange?

 b) How much concentrated orange should be mixed with 1 litre (1000 ml) of water?

Exercise 6.3C cont'd

3 Two people share all their costs in the ratio 2 to 3.

    a) If the first pays £400, how much does the second pay?

    b) If the second pays £150, how much does the first pay?

4 To make pink paint, red and white paint are mixed in the ratio 3 parts red to 5 parts white.

    a) How much white is mixed with 15 litres of red?

    b) How much red is mixed with 350 ml of white?

5 The ratio of the sides of two similar triangles A and B is 3 : 4.

    a) One side of A is 9 cm long. What is the length of the corresponding side of B?

    b) One side of B is 8·4 cm long. What is the length of the corresponding side of A?

Sharing in a given ratio

EXERCISE 6.4C

1 Split £1950 in the ratio 4 : 5 : 6.

2 Nasim and Andre share a bill in the ratio 2 : 3. The bill is £21·00.
How much does Andre pay?

3 Sue, Audrey and Aggie invest £70 000 between them in the ratio 2 : 3 : 5.
How much do they each invest?

4 To make mortar, sand and cement are mixed in the ratio 5 parts sand to 1 part cement.
How much of each is needed to make 12 kg of mortar?

5 Paint is mixed with 2 parts white to 3 parts black to make grey.
How much black is needed to make 2·5 litres of grey?

Equations with brackets

Equations with brackets

EXERCISE 7.1C

Solve these equations.

1 $2(x - 3) = 6$ **3** $3(x - 2) = 15$ **5** $2(3x - 4) = 4$

2 $3(2x + 1) = 27$ **4** $2(3x - 6) = 18$

Equations with the unknown on both sides

EXERCISE 7.2C

Solve these equations.

1 $3x - 2 = x + 2$ **3** $2x + 5 = 6 - 2x$ **5** $4(3x + 1) = 7x + 14$

2 $4x - 5 = 3x - 4$ **4** $2(3x - 1) = 4x + 5$

8 Powers and indices

Indices

Write these using indices.

1 $3 \times 3 \times 3 \times 3$ **3** $a \times a \times a \times a$ **5** $2 \times 2 \times 2 + 3 \times 3$

2 $4 \times 4 \times 4 \times 4 \times 4 \times 4$ **4** $b \times b + c \times c$

Substituting numbers into a formula

Find the value of y in each of these for the given x values.

1 $y = 2x + 1$ for   **a)** $x = 2$ **b)** $x = {}^-2$

2 $y = 3x - 1$ for   **a)** $x = 2$ **b)** $x = {}^-2$

3 $y = x^2 - 1$ for   **a)** $x = 2$ **b)** $x = {}^-2$

4 $y = 2x^2 + x$ for   **a)** $x = 2$ **b)** $x = {}^-3$

5 $y = x^2 - 2x + 3$ for   **a)** $x = 4$ **b)** $x = {}^-2$

9 Circles

EXERCISE 9.1C

Calculate the circumference of these circles.
Give the answers to 1 decimal place.

1 Diameter 4 cm   **3** Diameter 19·2 cm   **5** Radius 35·9 cm

2 Diameter 3·7 cm   **4** Radius 6·3 cm

Area of a circle

EXERCISE 9.2C

Calculate the area of these circles.
Give the answers to 1 decimal place.

1 Radius 4 cm   **3** Radius 1·9 cm   **5** Diameter 11 cm

2 Radius 3·7 cm   **4** Radius 6·3 cm

Scatter diagrams

Scatter diagrams

Draw a scatter diagram for each of these sets of data.

1

x	y
4	20
5	21
8	36
9	28
15	40
12	31
13	35
16	40
7	30

2

x	y
19	9
21	6
10	12
14	10
17	6
16	7
13	8
12	9
10	15

Correlation and lines of best fit

1 Comment on the correlation, if any, between x and y in Questions 1 and 2 of Exercise 10.1C.

2 These are the marks of 10 students in Form 10A in English and Geography.

English	59	69	41	62	45	85	50	65	77	48
Geography	59	64	50	61	55	80	60	72	75	54

a) Draw a scatter diagram to show this information.

b) Comment on the correlation between the marks in the two subjects.

Exercise 10.2C cont'd

   c) Use a line of best fit to estimate:

      i) the Geography mark of a student who scored 60 in English

      ii) the English mark of a student who scored 70 in Geography.

3 This table gives the average maximum temperature and the rainfall in June for 10 different cities.

Temperature (°C)	18	19	20	21	22	23	24	27	28	29
Rainfall (mm)	47	64	60	73	84	37	49	29	63	47

   a) Draw a scatter diagram to show this information.

   b) Comment on the correlation, if any, between the temperature and the rainfall.

   c) Another city has an average maximum temperature of 23°C in June. What can you deduce from the scatter diagram about its average rainfall?

11 **Multiplication and division of fractions**

Work these out.

1 $\frac{1}{2} \times 6$ **2** $\frac{1}{4} \times 10$ **3** $6 \times \frac{2}{3}$ **4** $\frac{1}{4} \times \frac{2}{3}$ **5** $16 \times \frac{5}{8}$

6 $\frac{1}{2} \div 2$ **7** $10 \div \frac{1}{5}$ **8** $\frac{1}{4} \div \frac{1}{8}$ **9** $\frac{1}{2} \div \frac{3}{4}$ **10** $\frac{2}{3} \div 8$

Work these out.

1   **a)** $\frac{1}{4} \times \frac{3}{5}$ **b)** $\frac{1}{3} \times \frac{1}{4}$

2   **a)** $\frac{3}{4} \times \frac{2}{3}$ **b)** $\frac{4}{5} \times \frac{1}{2}$

3   **a)** $\frac{3}{4} \times \frac{8}{9}$ **b)** $\frac{5}{6} \times \frac{3}{5}$

4   **a)** $\frac{1}{4} \div \frac{3}{5}$ **b)** $\frac{1}{5} \div \frac{3}{5}$

5   **a)** $\frac{1}{8} \div \frac{3}{4}$ **b)** $\frac{1}{6} \div \frac{3}{8}$

12 Negative numbers and decimals

Adding and subtracting negative numbers

EXERCISE 12.1C

1 $^-5 \times 4$

2 $^-4 + 3 - 2 - 1 + 1 + 3 + 4 - 5$

3 **a)** $\dfrac{^-5 + 1}{2}$ **b)** $\dfrac{4 - 9}{8 - 3}$

4 $(^-2 \times {}^-4) + (3 \times {}^-2)$

5 $(^-5 \times 4) - (^-2 \times 8)$

Decimals – a reminder

EXERCISE 12.2C

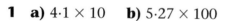

1 £4·37 + £5·23   **3** £8·46 + £5·79   **5** £6·23 + £3·74 − £4·66

2 £2·61 + £3·42   **4** £5·83 − £2·54

EXERCISE 12.3C

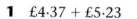

1 **a)** $4\cdot1 \times 10$ **b)** $5\cdot27 \times 100$ **c)** $32\cdot6 \times 100$ **d)** $0\cdot125 \times 1000$

2 **a)** $21\cdot4 \div 10$ **b)** $172\cdot5 \div 100$ **c)** $62\cdot3 \div 100$ **d)** $5\cdot14 \div 1000$

EXERCISE 12.4C

1 **a)** $1\cdot2 \times 4$ **b)** $2\cdot3 \times 0\cdot5$ **c)** $4\cdot6 \times 200$ **d)** $2\cdot5 \times 1\cdot2$ **e)** $1\cdot4 \times 0\cdot02$

2 Given $47 \times 53 = 2491$, find:

    a) $4\cdot7 \times 5\cdot3$ **b)** $4\cdot7 \times 5300$ **c)** $4\cdot7 \times 0\cdot053$ **d)** $0\cdot47 \times 5\cdot3$ **e)** 47×5300

EXERCISE 12.5C

1 $20.5 \div 5$ **2** $36.2 \div 2$ **3** $12.4 \div 4$ **4** $124.2 \div 3$ **5** $5.45 \div 5$

EXERCISE 12.6C

1 $0.24 \div 2$ **2** $14.2 \div 0.2$ **3** $3.5 \div 2.5$ **4** $3.6 \div 2.4$ **5** $5.6 \div 28$

13 Linear graphs I

Points in all four quadrants

EXERCISE 13.1C

1 On a grid, draw and label axes from $^-5$ to $+5$ for both x and y.
Plot these points on the graph: $A(1, 2)$, $B(^-2, 3)$, $C(5, {}^-2)$, $D(0, 4)$, $E(^-3, {}^-2)$.

2 On a grid, draw and label axes from $^-5$ to $+5$ for both x and y.
Draw and label the line for each of these equations.

$$x = {}^-4, \qquad x = 2, \qquad y = 4, \qquad y = {}^-3.$$

3 Draw the graph of $y = 2x$ for $x = {}^-3$ to $+3$.

4 Draw the graph of $y = 3x - 2$ for $x = {}^-2$ to $+4$.

5 Draw the graph of $y = 6 - 2x$ for $x = {}^-2$ to $+4$.

Harder straight-line equations

EXERCISE 13.2C

1 Draw the graph of $3x + 4y = 12$.

2 Draw the graph of $2x + 6y = 12$.

3 Draw the graph of $2y = 3x - 4$ for $x = {}^-2$ to 4.

14 Linear graphs II

Story graphs

EXERCISE 14.1C

1 This graph shows Michael's journey from Dorton to Canburn on a bicycle.

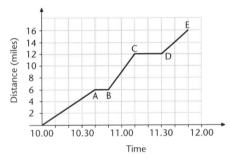

a) Which parts of the graph show Michael not moving?

b) What time did Michael get to Canburn?

c) How far did he travel altogether?

2 This graph shows the number of students in Form 10D at school each day during a week in June.

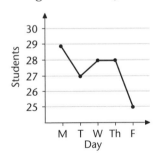

a) Which day did most students attend and how many were there?

b) Between which two days was there the biggest change in the number attending?

c) What was the average number of pupils attending per day?

Exercise 14.1C cont'd

3 A model plane was launched. It rose to a height of 25 metres in 30 seconds.
It climbed slowly at first and then faster.
It flew at a height of about 25 metres for 60 seconds.
It then dived to the ground in 5 seconds.

Make a sketch graph to illustrate this story.

Drawing triangles and different shapes

Drawing triangles

EXERCISE 15.1C

1 a) Make an accurate drawing of this triangle.

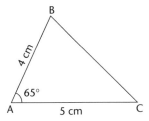

b) Measure the length of BC on your diagram.

2 a) Make an accurate drawing of this triangle.

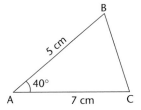

b) Measure the size of angle C on your drawing.

3 a) Make an accurate drawing of this triangle.

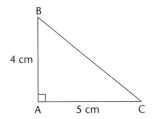

b) Measure the length of BC on your drawing.

EXERCISE 15.2C

1 a) Make an accurate drawing of this triangle.

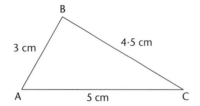

 b) Measure the size of angle A on your drawing.

2 a) Make an accurate drawing of this triangle.

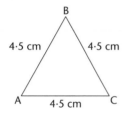

 b) What do you notice about the angles of this triangle.

3 a) Make an accurate drawing of this triangle.

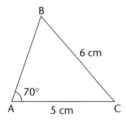

 b) Measure the length of AB on your drawing.

Chapter 15 Drawing triangles and different shapes

Exercise 15.2C cont'd

4 **a)** Make an accurate drawing of this triangle.

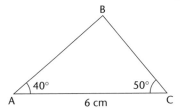

b) Measure the length of AB on your drawing.

Nets

EXERCISE 15.3C

1 Which of these nets can make a cube?

a)

b)

c)

d)

e)

2 Draw a net for each of these cuboids on squared paper.
All lengths are in centimetres.

a)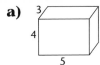

b)

c)

16 Areas

Area of a triangle

EXERCISE 16.1C

1 Find the areas of these triangles. All lengths are in centimetres.

a)

b)

c)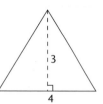

d)

e)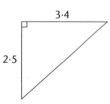

f)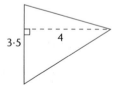

g)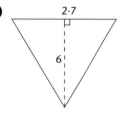

h)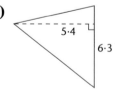

2 A triangle has vertices at (1, 2), (2, 5) and (8, 2).
Draw the triangle on squared paper and find its area.

Area of a parallelogram

1 Find the area of each of these parallelograms.

a)
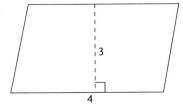

b)
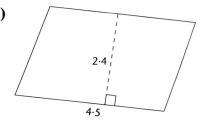

c)
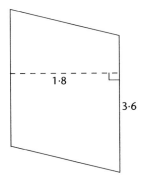

d)
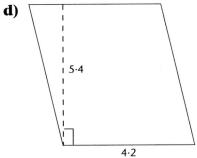

2 Find the values of x, y, and z.

a)
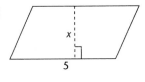

Area = 20 cm²

b)
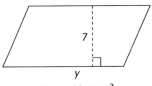

Area = 22·4 cm²

c)
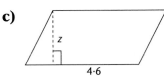

Area = 16·1 cm²

Area of a trapezium

EXERCISE 16.3C

1 Find the area of each of these trapezia.

a)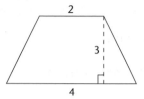

b)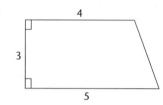

c)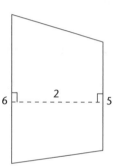

d)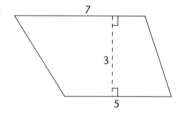

2 Find the values of x and y.

a)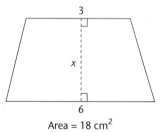

Area = 18 cm²

b)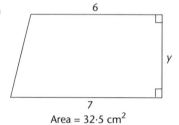

Area = 32·5 cm²

17 Volume

EXERCISE 17.1C

1 A cube has edges 5 cm long. Find the volume of the cube.

2 A box has height 10 cm, length 5 cm, width 3 cm. Find its volume.

3 A classroom is 6 metres long, 4 metres wide and 3 metres high.
   Work out its volume.

4 A biscuit tin is 12 cm long, 5 cm wide and 6 cm deep. Work out its volume.

5 **a)** Calculate the volumes of these cuboids. All lengths are in centimetres.

    i) 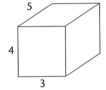   **ii)**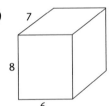

    b) Calculate the total surface areas of these cuboids.

18 Grouping data

Stem and leaf diagrams

1 These are the marks of 30 pupils in a test.

32	42	23	37	28	12	37	6	5	37
17	18	31	29	27	11	21	37	28	37
22	31	23	47	23	12	24	34	41	43

    a) Make a stem and leaf diagram of these marks.

    b) Use the diagram to find   **i)** the median mark   **ii)** the mode.

2 The ages of the first 25 men and the first 25 women to enter a supermarket on a Wednesday were recorded.

    Men:

52	62	73	37	69	62	77	76	65
47	47	48	61	39	27	51	21	47
58	57	61	74	82	81	64		

    Women:

62	61	63	37	23	52	44	64	51
53	52	42	33	77	49	41	84	82
71	64	40	67	61	52	54		

    a) Make a stem and leaf diagram for the ages of the men and the women.

    b) Find the median age for the men and for the women.

Mean, median and mode

EXERCISE 18.2C

1 For each of these sets of data, work out the mean, median and mode.

    a) 5, 4, 7, 7, 8, 11, 7, 6, 8, 9   **b)** 25, 27, 29, 22, 25

    c) 6, 7, 0, 8, 4, 7, 7, 1, 2, 3

2 Work out the mean, median and mode for this set of data.

Number	1	2	3	4	5	6	7	8	9	10
Frequency	3	2	4	5	7	2	0	1	0	1

Frequency tables

EXERCISE 18.3C

1 These are the heights, in centimetres, of 20 girls.

155	145	153	156	162
161	147	142	143	134
137	139	143	140	157
151	154	158	138	144

Using intervals $130 \leqslant h < 135$, $135 \leqslant h < 140$, and so on, make a frequency table of these heights.

2 These are the ages of 30 members of Dronfield choir club.

55	24	48	29	59	35
38	54	65	63	27	35
28	46	34	40	25	61
52	54	25	42	28	21
47	36	67	39	59	61

Chapter 18 *Grouping data*

STAGE 6

Exercise 18.3C cont'd

    a) Using groups $20 \leqslant x < 30$, and so on, make a frequency table of these ages.

    b) Draw the frequency polygon of these ages.

3 Thirty students were asked to keep a record of the time they spent on the computer in one week. These are the results in hours.

3	4	12	15	18
12·5	7	16	5·5	17
23	18	17·5	29	16
11·5	21·5	17	12·5	7·5
22	13·5	23	14	23
12	24·5	11	12	7

    a) Using appropriate intervals, make a frequency table of these times.

    b) Draw a frequency diagram of these times.

Chapter 18 *Grouping data*

19 Enlargements

EXERCISE 19.1C

Use squared paper to answer these questions.
In each case, copy the original diagram.

1 Make a '2 times' enlargement
of this shape.

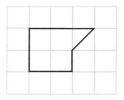

2 Enlarge this shape by scale factor 3,
from the origin.

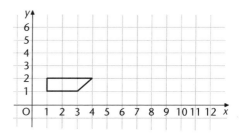

3 Enlarge this shape by scale factor 2,
from the centre, O.

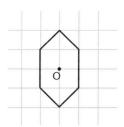

4 Describe fully the transformation
that maps triangle A onto triangle B.

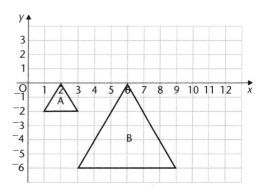

20 Transformations

EXERCISE 20.1C

Use squared paper to answer Questions 1 to 4.
In each case, copy the original diagram.

1 Reflect this shape in the line AB.

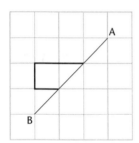

2 Rotate this shape through 90°
anticlockwise about the origin.

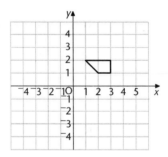

3 **a)** Translate triangle T 5 squares to the left and 1 down. Label it A.

b) Translate triangle A 4 squares to the right and 4 down. Label it B.

c) Describe the translation that will map triangle B onto triangle T.

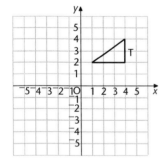

Exercise 20.1C cont'd

4 Rotate the shape through a quarter turn clockwise about A.

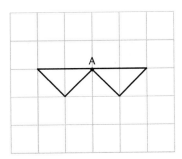

5 Describe fully the transformation that maps

a) A onto B   **b)** A onto C   **c)** A onto D   **d)** A to E.

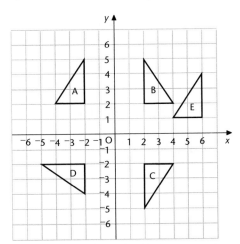

Chapter 20 Transformations

21 Compound measures

Compound units

EXERCISE 21.1C

1 Find the average speed of something that travels

   a) 120 miles in 5 hours

   b) 126 kilometres in 4 hours

   c) 75 miles in $2\frac{1}{2}$ hours

   d) 2000 metres in 80 seconds

   e) 400 metres in 64 seconds.

2 Find the density of an object with mass 600 g and volume 50 cm^3.

3 A town has an area of 15 square miles and its population is 90 000.
   Work out its population density in people per square mile.

4 A man walks at an average speed of 6 km per hour.
   How long does he take to walk 15 kilometres?

5 A car travels at 90 km per hour. How fast is this in metres per second?